4 T2

CONTENTS

GW00866750

Thomas and the Tinners
by Jill Paton Walsh

CREDITS

Published by Scholastic Ltd,
Villiers House,
Clarendon Avenue,
Leamington Spa,
Warwickshire CV32 5PR
Text © Sylvia Karavis and Catherine Byrne
© 1998 Scholastic Ltd
1 2 3 4 5 6 7 8 9 0   8 9 0 1 2 3 4 5 6 7

Author Judith Graham
Editor Joel Lane
Series designer Lynne Joesbury
Designer Rachel Warner
Illustrations Alan Marks
Cover illustration Alan Marks

Designed using Adobe Pagemaker

British Library Cataloguing-in-Publication Data
A catalogue record for this book is available
from the British Library.

ISBN 0-590-53834-9

ACKNOWLEDGEMENTS

Wayland Publishers Ltd and **David Higham
Associates Ltd** for the use of text, illustrations
and covers from *Thomas and the Tinners* by Jill
Paton Walsh © text 1995, Jill Paton Walsh
© illustrations 1995, Alan Marks (1995,
Macdonald Young Books).

INTRODUCTION

Thomas and the Tinners
by Jill Paton Walsh

WHAT IS THE PLOT OF THE STORY?

The story is set in a tin-mining community in Cornwall in the last century. Thomas, on his first morning in a tin mine, finds everything confusing and terrifying. At last lunchtime comes and he sits down to enjoy the Cornish pasty which Birdy, the ferryman's daughter, has given him. He is very surprised to be interrupted by a miniature miner, a Bucca, who wants a bite. Thomas takes pity on him and the Bucca gobbles up his pasty, but gives Thomas a wish in return. Unfortunately, Thomas wastes his wish. This happens again on the next two days. Hungry and frustrated, Thomas shares the problem with Birdy, and eventually he sees a way to use his wish to the benefit of everyone.

WHAT'S SO GOOD ABOUT THIS BOOK?

This story contains accurate information about tin-mining, and creates a strong sense of time and place. The reader experiences with Thomas the hardships and misery of hard work down a mine; but there is also magic in the story, which adds a lighter tone.

ABOUT THE AUTHOR

Jill Paton Walsh lives in Cambridge and has written many books, mostly for older children and adults. She is well known for historical novels such as *Grace*, the story of Grace Darling, and *A Parcel of Patterns*, set in 1665 (the time of the Great Plague). Her books are always well-researched, and she is very skilled in using the language and speech rhythms of other times.

Talking about wishes and magic

● Read the wishes that the three people below are making.

I wish I had finished my homework.

I wish I could be invisible whenever I wanted to be.

I wish there was no poverty in the world.

● All of us make wishes of different kinds all the time. What wishes have you made recently? Write them in the space below.

My wishes

● Sometimes what we wish for does actually happen. Sometimes we make wishes that could only come about through magic. Which of your wishes would need magic before they could happen? Write **M** beside them.

● In stories, it often happens that magical people, animals or objects are needed to make ordinary people's wishes come true. The columns below show some well-known magic makers. Add to these lists, perhaps from stories you know.

Special people	Special animals	Special objects
Elves	Spiders	Boots
Fairy godmothers	Cats	Cloaks

Talking about tin

The story which you are going to read is about wishes and magic, but it is also about more ordinary things like the world of work – and particularly the world of tin-mining. Here is some information about tin.

Cooked food is often preserved in tins. Food tins usually have a layer of tin covering iron or steel. Tin is much better than iron or steel for preserving food because it doesn't rust or spoil the taste of the food. Mixed with other metals, tin is used for various things including church bells and fuse-wire.

Tin doesn't come out of the ground as pure tin; it comes out as an **ore** or compound which has to be worked on to recover the tin. The ore is also known as tinstone or cassiterite. It is scattered through the rocks in the ground; and because it is black, the miners can see it against the paler rocks when they have dug a tunnel.

Tin has been mined since ancient times. Until the eighteenth century, Cornwall was the only important source of tin in the world. The Cornish tin mines mostly closed down in the early part of this century, and now nearly all tin comes from such countries as Australia, Thailand, Nigeria and Bolivia. You can still see the old tin mine buildings in parts of Cornwall, and some of them can be visited.

● Discuss the following questions together.
1. How do you think the tin miners could see what they were doing underground in the days before electric lighting?
2. How do you think tin miners stopped the holes and roofs of their tunnels from caving in?
3. The people working in a tin mine had different jobs. What jobs do you think there were?
4. If you were starting your first day at work down a tin mine, what would you be most anxious about?

The title and the covers

If you look at the title and illustration on the front cover of the book, you can guess who Thomas is and be fairly sure that he is the main character of the story. But the cover of a book should not give away too much. In *Thomas and the Tinners*, the title and the front cover illustration make you wonder what is happening and leave you with lots of questions, such as:

If the large character is Thomas, are the small people the tinners?
Why is Thomas eating such a large pie?
Is Thomas a giant? If he is not a giant, are those old men dwarves?
Why are they all looking at him?

You can talk about these questions, but you cannot know the answers until you have read the book.

There are other questions that you can try to guess the answers to by looking carefully and thinking hard, keeping the title in mind:

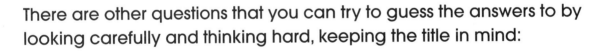

Why are all the characters wearing strange hats? What is sticking out of each hat?
What are those things hanging from the coat of one of the old men?
What are the shovel and rope for?
What is the orange cloth for?

● When you have discussed these questions, turn to the back cover. Look at the small illustration and read the blurb. You should now be more sure about some of your answers, but still mysteries remain. It's time to read the book and find out!

Thomas and Birdy

● Read Chapter 1. Like many opening chapters of novels, this chapter sets the scene by introducing us to the characters and describing where they live and work. It also starts off the story by bringing in the main character and a particular event. In this case, the main character is Thomas and the particular event is the conversation that he has with Birdy about the pasty.

● Read this conversation again. Discuss what each of them is likely to be thinking as they walk away, Birdy back to her house and Thomas up the hill to the mine. Continue the thought bubbles started below.

Poor Thomas. He didn't realise he had to have money for a pasty to eat at croust time.

That was nice of her. I won't forget to pay her on wage-day.

The world of work

Chapter 1 tells us about the work that Birdy and her father and mother do, and about the particular job of each of the tinners. Use information from the chapter to fill in the blanks in the chart below.

Name	Job	
Birdy	_____	
Birdy's mother	_____	
Birdy's father	_____	
Careful Jack	_____	
_____ Jack	holds the borer	
Hefty Jack	_____	
_____ Jack	lights the fuse to the gunpowder	
Standback Jack	_____	
_____ Jack	fetch and carry man	

● Perhaps there were many more 'Jacks' in the mine. In the chart below are some jobs that might have needed to be done in the mine, some of them perhaps done by women (would they be called 'Jill'?). Make up names for these additional Jacks or Jills. The first one has been done for you.

Name	Job
Thirst-quencher Jack	Keeping the drinking-water barrel full
_____	Replacing miners' burnt-out candles
_____	Checking and repairing ladders
_____	Checking and repairing baskets
_____	Inserting, checking and repairing wooden supports to hold up the roof
_____	Keeping an eye on the time
_____	Pumping out water from the mine

The magical Buccas

In Chapter 2, Thomas meets one of the Buccas for the first time. You won't find the word Buccas in a dictionary, but by the end of this chapter you will know quite a lot about them.

We find out about the Buccas in several ways. Jack the tribute man tells Thomas about them; the author describes what Thomas sees and hears when he encounters a Bucca; the illustrator draws a picture of a Bucca (page 16); and the Bucca, through his speech, tells us about himself.

● Using as much of this information as possible, write a short paragraph describing the Buccas for a reference book on magical creatures. Remember to include: what they are, their appearance, their size, their clothes, their way of speaking, their work, who can see them, their magic powers.

Buccas

Hard work and surprises

● Thomas's first day in the mine is divided into three distinct parts. Read Chapter 2 and then fill in the chart below, saying what happened in the three separate parts of the working day.

> Morning:
>
> Croust time:
>
> Afternoon:

● Thomas could never have imagined that his first day at work would be so extraordinary. But he doesn't tell anyone else about meeting the Bucca. Perhaps that night he doesn't feel sleepy – after all, he's had a long sleep in the afternoon. Imagine that he gets up during the night to write in his diary about the day's events. Write his diary entry, starting with the sentence below.

> Monday 13th April 1897
>
> First day at work and what a day!

Fear of the dark

● Read Chapter 3. Things do not improve very much for Thomas on his second day down the tin mine. The things that we know make him miserable are the hard work, his hunger and his fear of the dark.

About the darkness, Thomas says, 'I'm feared of the blackness down here' (page 22). Remember, almost the only light came from the candles in the tinners' hatcaps. As a new boy, Thomas would not have known how the mine was laid out and he must have been terrified.

● Discuss the dangers of working in the dark down the mine, remembering the information about the maze of tunnels, the 'tippy trembling ladders' and the 'holes in the floors' given in Chapter 1.

● Now imagine that all the tinners gave Thomas advice about coping in the dark. Fill in the speech bubbles with things they say to him.

Pasties, Buccas and wishes

When you have read Chapter 3, you will see that it repeats the story pattern set up in Chapter 2. However, there are some changes.

● Fill in brief details for Chapter 3 in the chart below, as is shown for Chapter 2.

Repeated item	Chapter 2 details	Chapter 3 details
Pasties	The pasty was small and was almost completely eaten by the Bucca.	
Why Thomas offered his pasty	Thomas felt that the Bucca had a ravenous longing on his face.	
Thomas's wish	Thomas wished it was time to go home.	

● You know enough about stories to predict how this pattern is likely to develop in the next chapter. Before you read Chapter 4, fill in the chart below with your predictions about what will happen.

Repeated item	What I think will happen in Chapter 4
Pasties	
Why Thomas offered his pasty	
Thomas's wish	

More pasties, Buccas and wishes

● When you have read Chapter 4, look back at the predictions you wrote on page 12.

● You probably wrote that the pasty would be even bigger. **But** did you guess that it would be as thick as a feather pillow? Probably not, as that sort of detail is special to the author. However, you may also have used a simile to describe the pasty. If you didn't, here is your chance!

Thomas's pasty was as big as _____

_____

● You probably wrote that Thomas was sorry when he saw the Buccas' hungry faces. **But** the author changed the detail here. How did she make it different? Write in the space below.

When the Bucca asked for a bite, Thomas _____

_____

_____

● When you predicted Thomas's wish, you probably thought he would choose something to make his day less miserable. **But** it is unlikely that you had exactly the same idea as the author. Write what Thomas wished for in the space below.

When Thomas wished for another pasty, the Buccas said

_____

so Thomas had the chance to wish again. He wished

_____

● How will the pattern of the story develop in the next chapter? Read on and see!

Too much to bear

In Chapter 4, Thomas at last decides to tell somebody about what is happening in the mine. It was a particularly awful day for him for several reasons:

1. He had hoped that the huge pasty would mean some was left for him, but half a dozen Buccas suddenly appeared and finished it off.
2. He had his wish granted in a terrifying way.
3. He became lost in the mine and he had to shout until he was found.
4. He was desperately hungry.
5. He had to bear the kindly-meant words of Standback Jack.

● Discuss why these experiences were particularly dreadful for Thomas. Perhaps you have also been bitterly disappointed, afraid in the dark, lost or very hungry, or have had to listen to someone giving you advice who didn't understand the situation. Talk about these experiences and then finish the following sentences:

I think the worst part of Thomas's day was _____

_____

_____

_____

I felt something like Thomas felt when _____

_____

_____

_____

● Think about Birdy's father's words to Thomas at the end of Chapter 4:

'Doesn't do to get across a fairy miner,' said Birdy's father. 'And they could do with some Buccas' luck up there. The tin lode* is nearly worked out, and there won't be livings for much longer.'

*A **lode** is a mass of rock with enough tin ore in it to be worth digging out.

When a chapter ends with words such as these which introduce a totally new idea, you know that you, as a reader, must pay attention because the author has written them for a good reason. Thomas will also have paid attention to these words.

● Imagine that the conversation went on for some time longer, with Thomas asking Birdy's parents lots of questions. In a group of three or four, continue the conversation below.

Scene: Outside Birdy's cottage.
Characters: Birdy's mother and father, Birdy, Thomas.

THOMAS: *What do you mean by Buccas' luck?*

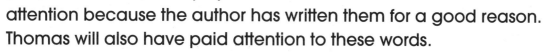

The final wish

● Read up to the point when Jack the tribute man breaks the news to the tinners about the mine being all worked out (page 37). Everything you have been thinking about in previous chapters should enable you to predict what will happen now. Write your prediction here:

What I think will happen now is

● Read on! How close were you? Now you know what Buccas' luck is.

● Chapter 5 ends with the line: 'Thomas rubbed his eyes and went to tell the others.' Because the author wants to get on with her story, and because she does not want to repeat things, what Thomas said and how the tinners received his news is left to our imaginations. Write down what you think Thomas said to the tinners. His speech to them is started off for you below.

'Jack, Jack, all of you Jacks! Stop your hammering! Come with me!

The end of the story

● Read Chapter 6. This is a very short chapter, but it makes a great many links back to the rest of the book. For example:

● 'Prospect Jack' links back to the name 'Prentice Jack' which Thomas was given in Chapter 1;

● 'stayed in Cornwall' links back to Tribute Jack's warning about having to go overseas in Chapter 5;

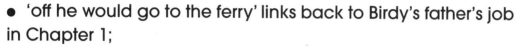

● 'staying lucky' links back to Birdy's father's comments about needing luck in Chapter 4;

● 'off he would go to the ferry' links back to Birdy's father's job in Chapter 1;

● 'Birdy and her mother would have ready an oven-busting pasty' links back to the pasties made by Birdy and her mother in many of the previous chapters.

● Find the links between these three quotes from Chapter 6 and earlier passages:

'Thomas would pay for it with a golden guinea' links back to

_____

_____

(look in Chapter 1)

'I'm a man that pays my debts' links back to

_____

_____

(look in Chapter 5)

'And there's some that can't fashion food' connects with

_____

_____

(look in Chapter 4)

● All these connections round the book off well, though you may still want to know one or two things. Write your feelings about this final chapter on another sheet of paper.

Job advertisement

● Imagine that, before the story began, this advertisement appeared in Thomas's local newspaper, *The Cornish Echo*:

Tin mine vacancy
Young person wanted to fetch and carry in local tin mine. Must be a hard worker and not afraid of the dark. Wages at the end of each working week.
Apply to Jack the Tribute man.*

* The tribute man was the miner who was generally in charge of the mine.

● Now write Thomas's letter applying for the job. He will probably include:

- his age;
- why he wants the job;
- why he thinks he will be good at it;
- a few questions.

10, Helstone Cottages,
Tregowan,
Cornwall.

3rd April, 1897

Dear Jack the Tribute man,

Yours sincerely.
Thomas Talgarth

Gunpowder!

● Re-read Chapter 1, page 7. Then look again at the picture on page 9. One of the walking miners is probably Careful Jack. Imagine that in his bag is a box of gunpowder with instructions on the side. Unfortunately, half the words are worn away or covered in dirt from the mine, and no one can read them any more. Can you fill in the missing words?

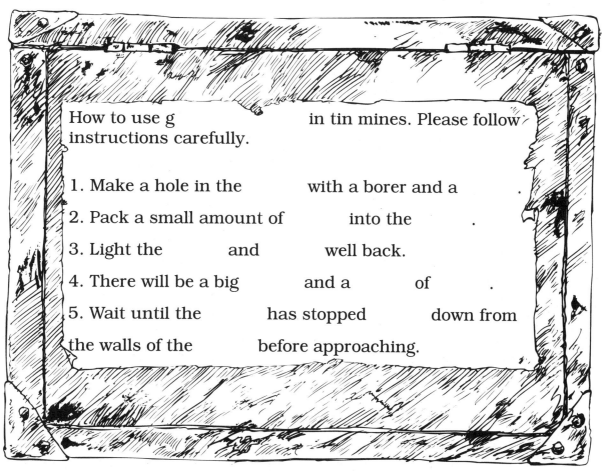

How to use g   in tin mines. Please follow instructions carefully.

1. Make a hole in the   with a borer and a

2. Pack a small amount of   into the   .

3. Light the   and   well back.

4. There will be a big   and a   of   .

5. Wait until the   has stopped   down from the walls of the   before approaching.

You will not be surprised to hear that many miners were killed or injured in gunpowder accidents, even when they followed instructions carefully. The main danger lay in the fuse, which sometimes burnt down so quickly that the miners did not have time to get clear. In the 19th century, William Bickford invented a long, thick fuse made from rope, with gunpowder poured into its centre. This fuse saved so many lives that it was called the safety fuse, and it remained in use for over 130 years.

● Can you find out more about William Bickford? Do some research and record your findings on another sheet of paper.

Turning facts into a story

● Re-read the following two paragraphs from the start of Chapter 2:

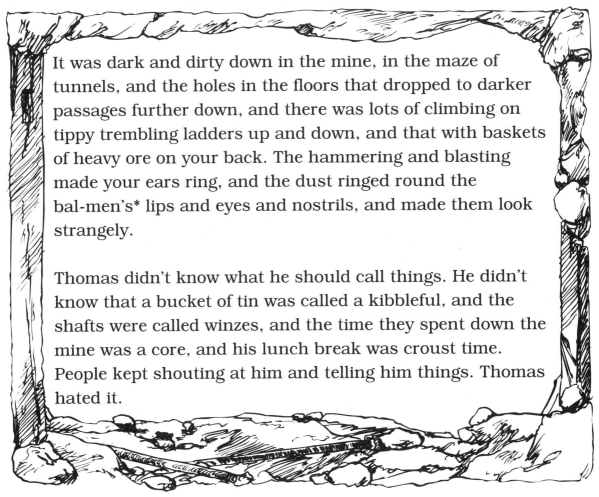

It was dark and dirty down in the mine, in the maze of tunnels, and the holes in the floors that dropped to darker passages further down, and there was lots of climbing on tippy trembling ladders up and down, and that with baskets of heavy ore on your back. The hammering and blasting made your ears ring, and the dust ringed round the bal-men's* lips and eyes and nostrils, and made them look strangely.

Thomas didn't know what he should call things. He didn't know that a bucket of tin was called a kibbleful, and the shafts were called winzes, and the time they spent down the mine was a core, and his lunch break was croust time. People kept shouting at him and telling him things. Thomas hated it.

*Bal *is an old term for mine.*

The author has clearly done some research on tin-mining. She explains to her readers some of the specialist terms: *kibble, winzes, a core, croust time.* She has also found out about what a tin mine looked like and some details of the tin mining process. She helps us to understand all this by showing it to us through Thomas's eyes.

● Now scan the whole book to find more specialist mining terms. You should be able to find at least six more. Put all the specialist terms that you have found onto the computer in alphabetical order, with a definition of each. For example: **croust time** (n.) lunch break during a working shift.

A major problem in a mine is the danger that the roof of a tunnel will cave in. If you cut a passage through rock and then use explosives to widen out an area so that tin ore can be chipped out of the rock, the ground above your head needs to be supported. If the rock is very rich in ore, you'll want to chip nearly all of it away, so the need for good props to hold the roof up is even greater.

Here are some of the specialist terms used by the timber-men in the mines:

- **pillar** – a column of rock allowed to stand to support the roof.
- **stull** – a roof of timbers fixed under the hanging rock to prevent it falling in.
- **stull-pieces** – the pieces of timber that make up the stull.
- **stope** – the opened-out area (rather like a cave) from which the ore is cut.
- **prop** – a single piece of timber, usually placed vertically between the roof and the floor of a stope; on its own, a prop can only support a very small section of roof.
- **wedge** – a piece of wood for hammering into a gap at the top of a prop to keep it tight.

● Now become an author. Use what you have learned about tin mines to write a story paragraph in which Thomas helps the timbermen to go round the stopes, checking the timber work. You can have as much or as little danger in your story as you like.

Thomas and his wishes

● Fill in this chart to show **all** the wishes that Thomas makes, and what the result of each wish was.

Chapter 2 Thomas meets and feeds a Bucca.

First wish:

Result:

Chapter 3 Thomas feeds two Buccas.

Second wish:

Result:

Chapter 4 Thomas feeds half a dozen Buccas.

Third wish:

Result:

Chapter 5 Thomas feeds a dozen or more Buccas.

Last wish:

Result:

● What was the main difference between Thomas's last wish and the previous three?

Thomas's last wish was different from the others because

● In many stories that you may know, a character is offered wishes and somehow wastes them. Thomas wastes his first three wishes, but he is lucky: he is allowed one more, and this time he does not waste it. Look back at the first three wishes that Thomas makes. Discuss with your group why these wishes were wasted.

● Now imagine that it was not until the **fifth** time that Thomas made the right kind of wish. In other words, there was an extra wasted wish before he wished for more tin. Now invent the extra wish. You can either write a whole extra chapter (which would come between Chapters 4 and 5) or continue from the lines given below. Try to use your knowledge of tin-mining in what you write.

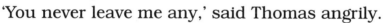

And before he could say a word, his huge pasty was gone, right down to the crust once more.

'You never leave me any,' said Thomas angrily.

'But you get a wish,' said one of the Buccas. Thomas thought about it.

'I wish,' he said, 'that

A message from the Buccas

● Look again at the Buccas' words to Thomas when they stop him eating the pasties:

'Not so fast!
Not so hasty!
Give us a bite of that there pasty!
We be mortal hungry!
We be a-dying down here!'

The Buccas speak with a definite rhythm, using repeated phrases and sometimes using rhymes. They also use words and expressions which are rarely heard nowadays or are part of a dialect, and use words in an unusual position in the sentence. Throughout *Thomas and the Tinners*, the author makes use of unusual words and expressions. You have probably had to ask or guess the meanings of some of them.

● Imagine that the Buccas write little thank-you letters or poems to Thomas each time he sends huge pasties down the mine-shaft to them. Write such a message in the box below. Work on it (using scrap paper) until you feel that the language sounds old-fashioned and unusual and has the right kind of rhythm. You might like to use some of these words and expressions from the story:

morsel	ravened	starvling
look strangely	bannock	feared
staunched	platter	atop
mainly good	guzzle	fair greedy
vasty	runtle	a likely lode
fashion food	pined	yammer

To Thomas (Prospect Jack)

from the Buccas

No one but Thomas

● *Why was Thomas and no one else able to see the Buccas?*
Here are some answers to this question from readers of the book. Which do you agree with? Tick the one closest to how you feel and then add a comment of your own.

'Thomas is the youngest tinner, so only he can see the Buccas. When another tinner comes, another apprentice, then Thomas won't be able to see the Buccas any more, but the new person who is younger than him will.' ☐

'I think Thomas could see the Buccas because he was poor but honest. He didn't even have a penny when he came on his first day at work and he wasn't even going to take a pasty, but he promised to pay for it at the end of the week.' ☐

'If Thomas hadn't shared his pasty with the Bucca on his first day, he'd never have seen the Buccas again and they wouldn't have shown him the tin. They were testing to see how generous he was. He couldn't help feeling sorry for the ravenous starving Buccas.' ☐

I think: _____

_____

_____

_____

● *Do you think Thomas will ever see the Buccas again?*
Make sure you give reasons for your opinion. Maybe the very last illustration in the book will influence what you think.

I think Thomas will/will not see the Buccas again, because

_____

_____

_____

What do you think?

● Think back to your discussion about the covers of the book before you began reading. Now, when you look at the front cover illustration, you have no problem in understanding all the details of the picture. Can you say exactly where this scene comes in the book?

_____

● You may think that the title of the book should have been *Thomas and the Buccas*. Why do you think this would not have been as successful a title, even though it might have been a more accurate description of the story? Give at least two reasons.

_____

_____

● If the book were reprinted with a different cover illustration, what would you like to see? On a separate sheet of paper, **either** draw an alternative cover **or** write instructions for the illustrator.

● Now choose **one** of the following to do, using a tape recorder.
● Imagine you are talking to Jill Paton Walsh. Tell her about what you thought and felt while you were reading and working on her book. Mention the title if you want to, and any other points that have interested you.
● Imagine you are talking to Alan Marks. Tell him what you thought and felt about his illustrations, and how much they contributed to your enjoyment of the book. Were there any parts of the story that you felt deserved an illustration, but didn't have one?

USING THIS BOOK

ORGANISING THE READING OF *THOMAS AND THE TINNERS*

The first two activities in the **Ways in** section of this book are designed to be carried out before the children see or read *Thomas and the Tinners*. The third activity in this section is focused on the cover of the Macdonald Young Books paperback.

The novel can then be read chapter by chapter. Each of the six chapters is supported by activities in the **Making sense** section. There are two activities for Chapter 1, two for Chapter 2, two for Chapter 3, three for Chapter 4, one for Chapter 5 and one for Chapter 6. This structure helps children to look closely at the way the narrative is constructed and to use their developing knowledge of the story to predict confidently, anticipate events, recognise patterns and make connections.

Some of these activities are also designed to slow down the reading at certain points, helping the children to appreciate the significance of new information or the atmosphere being created. Sometimes readers' first-hand experience is elicited to illuminate what they are reading.

The **Developing ideas** section prompts children to re-read and to think beyond the immediate text through consideration of (for example) possible events before and after the story, the background of place and time in which the book is set, the specialist terms used in the book, the author's use of local idiom and the underlying moral of the story.

The final **Evaluation** activity suggests several ways in which children can stand back from the book and express their final thoughts and feelings about it.

It is not expected that every child in the class will work through every activity. The teacher should select activities which will appeal to the class, extend them appropriately, and confirm and consolidate the learning achieved. If different groups work on different activities and then report back on their work to the whole class, then everybody shares the benefits of each group's experience.

CLASSROOM MANAGEMENT AND SUPPORT

Thomas and the Tinners is a wonderful book to read aloud. Ideally, it should be read by the teacher to the whole class in a series of carefully-planned sessions. The teacher will have decided which activities are appropriate for the passage or chapter being read, and should preface each task with discussion. If there are children in the class whose reading is enjoyed by the rest of the class, they could share the task of reading out the book. In order

for such reading to hold the attention of the whole class, time should be given for preparation and practice.

Many children need (and will enjoy) more than one chance to hear the story. There is no commercial recording (as yet) of *Thomas and the Tinners*, but teachers could prepare their own; this is not as time-consuming as it sounds, and is an enjoyable activity. The taped version then becomes a permanent resource.

If time allows, children can re-read chapters to each other in pairs or small groups prior to or during the activities. Individual, silent, private reading is also appropriate when the text needs to be revisited. Activities which require access to *Thomas and the Tinners* are marked with the icon. It is advisable to have about six copies of the book available, so that groups and pairs can work independently. If the whole class is working on the book, ensure that some children at least are working on activities that do not require close attention to the text, so that each copy can be shared between a pair or group of children.

Nearly all of the activities are designed to be worked on (at least initially) by a group or pair. Alternatively, most of the activities can be adapted for whole-class discussion before the groups commence work. Writing required within the activities can be undertaken by individuals; but, as always, children will benefit from working with a partner.

DIFFERENTIATION

As was indicated above, there is no need to expect every child to work through all the activities. The teacher will be able to judge which children need which type of activity at any given time. In general, the activities on pages 11, 13, 14, 15, 17, 20, 21, 24, and 26 are more challenging. When working on these activities, less confident readers and writers may need the support of the teacher or other children with more experience.

The teachers will also want to make her/his own judgements of when the modelling of an activity is appropriate. For instance, the activity on page 9 works well if the teacher demonstrates how to comb the text for information and shares an enlarged version of a reference book entry with the class.

The teachers' notes (see pages 29-32) suggest some extension activities. These are additional or alternative ideas which could be explored by individuals, pairs or groups, or by the teacher working with the whole class. These activities may involve discussion, artwork, research, wider reading, drama and role-play, story writing, display, book-making and carrying out surveys.

TIME-SCALE

An uninterrupted reading out loud of *Thomas and the Tinners* takes about an hour. It is recommended that the process of reading the book and working on the activities take up approximately 2 hours a week over two or three weeks. If extension ideas are undertaken, the time could easily be doubled.

This way of working gives children a chance to experience a significant encounter with a book, and time to appreciate its qualities without their enjoyment of the book suffering. It is to be hoped that a positive experience with a short novel such as *Thomas and the Tinners* will enable children to approach and appreciate longer novels as they grow older.

STRENGTH OF THE BOOK

The story of *Thomas and the Tinners* has some of the power and universal appeal of a fairy tale, with the added attraction that its setting has a basis in historical fact. As with Jill Paton Walsh's other novels, the setting is well-researched and convincing but the writing is not didactic. Most children will find Thomas's experiences both 'magical' and moving. The book's structure is both reassuring in its repetitive aspects and fresh in its surprises. The illustrations are vivid and supportive.

The unfamiliar vocabulary in the book will challenge many children; but the author is well able to place the difficult words in explanatory contexts, and in any case most children will enjoy the new words and their strangeness.

TEACHING POTENTIAL OF *THOMAS AND THE TINNERS*

The Skills Grid on the inside back cover indicates the reading response skill areas covered by each activity. *Thomas and the Tinners* also offers the following learning opportunities:
- **Writing:** thought tracking; a reference book entry; a diary entry; dialogue; personal reflections; a drama script; a job application letter; instructions; a database; an extra chapter; an informal letter or poem; a personal opinion.
- **Literary understanding and response:** understanding of narrative patterning in the genre of the traditional story; expansion of 'gaps' left by the author; appreciation of the author's ability to convey information; relating the story to one's own experience; making connections between points in the story; putting the story into a wider context, including its historical basis.
- **Responding to language:** responding to the author's literary, dialect and specialist language; creating stylistically comparable text; appreciating figures of speech and other literary effects.

Cross-curricular links:
- history – 19th-century tin-mining;
- art and design – models, plans, drawings;
- geography – locating tin-mining regions;
- science – examining the properties of tin and the uses to which tin is put.

RECOMMENDED PREVIOUS TEACHING

The children will need to be familiar with the following skills and knowledge.

1. Reading: bringing personal experience to bear on understanding a book; re-reading; scanning text for information; close reading of text and illustrations; examining rhythm, rhyme and scansion in poems; story terms such as *character*, *patterning*, *plot links*, *gaps in text*; research using reference books.

2. Writing: conjecturing and predicting; writing in groups, with one member as scribe; drawing on knowledge of traditional stories; writing diary entries, playscripts, poems, letters (both formal and informal), direct speech, reference book entries, instructions; using facts within narrative writing; compiling a computer database; compiling a survey.

3. Speaking and listening: structured group discussion; role-play.

If children do not have experience and knowledge of some of the above items, the activities in this book could be used as an introduction.

BACKGROUND KNOWLEDGE AND RESOURCES

The more the children can find out about tin-mining, the better able they will be to imagine Thomas's life. Several illustrated pamphlets and books on this theme, written by J.A. Buckley (such as *The Cornish Mining Industry* and *Cornish Mining – Underground*), are available from Tor Mark Press, United Downs Industrial Estate, St Day, Redruth, Cornwall TR16 5HY. Otherwise, good encyclopaedias will have entries on tin-mining, and libraries or museums may have specialist titles. In addition, *Hocus Pocus*, compiled by Lesley Young and illustrated by Babette Cole (Hamish Hamilton, 1984), is a useful source of folklore on 'little people' and magical themes.

When working on the activities, the children will need access to traditional stories, encyclopaedias, dictionaries and illustrated reference books and cassette recorders. Copies of job advertisements, instructions of various kinds, headed notepaper, maps, labelled drawings and poems will also be useful to display. The books listed on page 32 will be useful for wider reading.

TEACHERS' NOTES

WAYS IN
TALKING ABOUT WISHES AND MAGIC
Aim: to relate a major aspect of the story to experience, imagination and reading.
Teaching points: this activity should be carried out before the book is read or looked at. Children may wish to discuss the reasons why most fairy stories and folktales have magic in them. They may suggest that magic is an attractive fantasy for people who are very poor or in trouble. Other workers of magic that children may recall from stories include: wizards, witches, trolls, tricksters, giants, gnomes, dwarves, fairies, speaking fish, dragons, horses, wolves, frogs, snakes, spiders, crowns, belts, golden balls, wands, pots, lamps, bottles, purses.
Extension: stories often include the idea of three wishes being used either wisely or unwisely. The children could find and categorise examples of these stories. (See further reading list on page 32.)

TALKING ABOUT TIN
Aims: to learn background information; to think about the practical realities of tin-mining.
Teaching points: this activity should be carried out before the book is read or looked at. The information provided on the sheet relates to what tin is used for, how it is extracted and the history of tin-mining. These facts should lead children to consider the practicalities of working in a tin mine; their suggestions may be confirmed by seeing the cover of the book and/or reading the first two chapters. Appropriate resources such as early photographs, mining artefacts or objects made of tin would be useful to display as background material.
Extension: children could undertake further research (encyclopaedias might be useful). They could visit a suitable exhibition or museum.

THE TITLE AND THE COVERS
Aims: to reinforce the concept of a main character; to make deductions from the cover illustration; to develop interest in the story.
Teaching points: harvest all suggestions uncritically. Encourage the children to notice other aspects of the cover: larger type for main character's name, author's name in different colour from title, and so on. Children should notice that in the illustration all eyes are on the main character, who is in the centre of the picture and larger than the other figures. The children's unresolved questions should provoke their interest in the book.
Extension: children may like to compare this cover with the covers of other books, looking at the type styles, layout and illustrations.

MAKING SENSE
THOMAS AND BIRDY
Aim: to imagine characters' thoughts, based on empathy and knowledge of the story so far.
Teaching points: it may be necessary for the whole class to discuss the possible contents of one thought bubble before individuals are ready to tackle the task. Children may suggest that Birdy, for instance, is thinking that Thomas's appetite will be the same as hers since he is no taller than her; that he is unfamiliar with the food arrangements; that he doesn't know what he's in for in the mine; that he may become a friend; or that she may be in trouble if he doesn't pay.
Extension: drama will help the children to extend the characters' lines of thought. In particular, thought tracking (freezing the action at a particular point and asking a child in role to state her/his thoughts) will be useful.

THE WORLD OF WORK
Aims: to scan text for information and represent it; to invent further names, using the model given.
Teaching points: discuss with the children how the author has created the working names of the tinners. The name may use a quality of the character, what he says or does, or the object that he is associated with at work. Thus, for example, someone who replaces the candles could be Light-giver Jack or Keep-'em-burning Jack or Waxy Jack.
Extension: in fact, most of the women in tin-mining communities worked only on the surface and had different jobs from the miners. Children could research these jobs and invent names for the surface workers.

THE MAGICAL BUCCAS
Aims: to read closely for a specific purpose; to represent information using a reference book format.
Teaching points: it may be useful to share various reference book entries (on any topic) with the children to give them a model. *Hocus Pocus* compiled by Lesley Young (see 'Background knowledge and resources' on page 28) would be useful here, as it contains entries on such creatures as elves and leprechauns – and even on the 'knockers', little people of actual tin-mining legend.
Extension: children could return to their reference book entries on the Buccas and amend or expand them when they have finished reading the book.

The reading of this book creates scope for the compilation of a small technical and/or dialect dictionary by the children. (See notes on 'Turning facts into a story' on page 31.)

HARD WORK AND SURPRISES

Aims: to chart a sequence of events; to represent information in an imaginative way.

Teaching points: discussion may centre on whether Thomas's encounter with the Bucca might have put his morning's misery out of his mind. Children may also question the likelihood of Thomas's being able to write, let alone being able to afford a diary!

Extension: children may like to research (or invent) other myths and legends which deal with experiences of toiling in a difficult world – for example, life as a woodcutter, blacksmith, cook, shoemaker, fisherman or seamstress.

FEAR OF THE DARK

Aim: to account for Thomas's feelings through empathy and close reference to the text.

Teaching points: encourage the children to describe their own experiences of being afraid in the dark. Then remind them that Thomas has to move around in the dark in a place which is unfamiliar to him and is full of real dangers.

Extension: drama work with the children working in the dark or blindfolded would be an ideal way to recreate Thomas's experiences of darkness. Looking at old photographs of mines will give an idea of the terrain, though it should be remembered that the miners never saw their mine in such a bright light as a photographic flash.

PASTIES, BUCCAS AND WISHES

Aims: to explore patterning in the story; to base predictions on this structure.

Teaching points: the relevant details from Chapter 3 are that the pasty was 'man-sized'; it was eaten in 'two tremendous bites... right down to the dry hard crust'; Thomas felt that the two Buccas looked 'pined and hungry'; Thomas wished he could see the daylight. Children's predictions should encompass these ideas: the pasty is still bigger (or he is given more than one pasty); there are more Buccas than before; they seem even more plaintive; and Thomas's wish is equally short-term.

Extension: the children's suggestions for Thomas's wish could be developed into another incident in the story. For instance, if Thomas wishes he could see in the dark, he could come to regret it as he is rushed off his feet illuminating everybody's tasks. The new episodes could be compiled as a class book.

Encourage children to share their memories of traditional stories in which wishes are offered. 'The Fisherman and His Wife' is a good (and equally moral) example of a story in which the repeated pattern is fixed, but significant changes are made in the details.

MORE PASTIES, BUCCAS AND WISHES

Aims: to analyse how the author makes changes in her basic story pattern; to appreciate how different similes are used to emphasise changes.

Teaching points: the concept of a simile may need discussion. The evocative power of similes in the text could be discussed – for example, the pasty 'as thick as a mattress', the Bucca 'dancing around like a spinning top or a boy on a birthday' or the Buccas 'turning... transparent as fire'.

Extension: much of the author's distinctive language repays attention. The children's attention could be drawn to instances of metaphor ('a scrap of a boy'; 'a pale disc of light'; 'a round, blue platter made of sky'), alliteration ('tippy trembling ladders'; 'curve of crust'; 'snip, snap'; 'gnawing his knuckles'; 'greedy great talking mackerel'; 'their lovely likely lode') and idiomatic phrases ('not knee high to him'; 'an oven-busting pasty').

TOO MUCH TO BEAR

Aims: to reflect on the experiences of the main character; to justify an opinion; to relate text to personal experience.

Teaching points: in Chapter 4, Thomas experiences an accumulation of sorrows; this raises complex issues for discussion. You may need to support children in their understanding of what Thomas goes through, especially when discussing the frustrating effect on him of Standback Jack's comments at the end of the day. Encourage the children to draw comparisons with their own experiences, but be sensitive to any children who may find discussion of these themes distressing.

Extension: drama work will help children to recreate Thomas's frightening experience of being carried through low tunnels and emerging, giddy, at the mouth of the adit (the drain from the mine) on the edge of a cliff. Some children might like to construct a map or a model of the tin mine.

THOMAS EXPLAINS TO BIRDY

Aims: to extend the text, filling a gap in it, through imaginative dramatic reconstruction.

Teaching points: some sense of the poverty that would face this community if the mine closed down needs to be conveyed to the class. Children could be encouraged to speculate that the miners may have attributed past accidents to their having offended the Buccas in some way. The dialogue produced by each group should be scribed by one child.

Extension: Birdy's parents may well have stories to tell of good or bad luck, hardship, accidents and tragedy. Children could invent and tell a story, in the voice of Birdy's father or mother, about the past history of the mine – including the role played by the Buccas.

THE FINAL WISH
Aims: to make predictions and check them against text; to revisit text through retelling.
Teaching points: this is a further 'filling a gap in the text' activity. It should be possible, at this time, to discuss with the children how it is unnecessary for an author to spell out everything, and how we must do the work in our heads to fill the 'gaps' as we read.
Extension: children could look back at their own written stories to see whether they could cut out unnecessary details or explanations, making the reader's experience more enjoyable. They could aim to do this in new stories.

THE END OF THE STORY
Aims: to make textual links and connections through scanning particular chapters; to express an opinion on the way the story ends.
Teaching points: the five connections listed may need to be talked through to ensure the understanding of the whole class. The missing links to be found are as follows: (1) Thomas not having a penny to pay for his first pasty; (2) the Buccas saying that they always pay their debts; (3) the Buccas saying that 'what they can't do' is make food. Provide additional paper for the children to write their comments on the final chapter. Typical comments might be to query Thomas's change of working name, or to ask what happens to Birdy.
Extension: do the children feel that all the loose ends have been tied up in a satisfying way? The last we hear about the Buccas, for instance, is that they have turned into flickering flames and blown out before Thomas's eyes. Children may wish to add a line or two about what becomes of them.

DEVELOPING IDEAS
JOB ADVERTISEMENT
Aims: to speculate on events 'outside' the text; to write a job application letter.
Teaching points: in reality, such a job would probably have been 'advertised' by word of mouth, and Thomas would not have needed (and would not have been competent) to write a letter of application. Discussing these issues with the class should not invalidate the activity.
Extension: children could role-play an interview between Thomas and Jack the tribute man, and/or Thomas talking through the job application with his parents. Children could research and discuss the issues surrounding the employment of young people (not much older than themselves) in manual work.

GUNPOWDER!
Aims: to read closely for information and represent it in a different form; to research a historical topic.
Teaching points: this activity offers scope (especially around November 5th) for a general discussion on the uses and dangers of gunpowder. Make sure that the children have access to suitable texts in order to find out about the inventor of the safety fuse.
Extension: some children may like to create the powder-box with its worn instructions. More able children could investigate the history and functioning of other inventions used in mining, such as the water-pump.

TURNING FACTS INTO A STORY
Aims: to read closely; to scan text; to demonstrate understanding; to see how an author informs while narrating; to create a database; to use given facts in a new story.
Teaching points: the strangeness of the specialist vocabulary can be overcome by making frequent reference to these terms, encouraging the class to make labelled drawings or models of a tin mine and setting up role play between, for example, the tribute man and the timberman. The convention of using 'n.' for 'noun' in dictionary entries may also need explanation.

Specialist tin-mining terms that the children may find in the book include: ingots, borer, seam, croust-bag, adit, ore, outfall, lode, bore holes, fetching up, coming to grass. The children's new episodes could be compiled as a class book.
Extension: The children could use the terms they have learned to produce a labelled drawing of the mine. It may help them to look again at Alan Marks's illustrations, and to check with their group that they understand the terms in the same way.

If individual children become fascinated by the world of tin-mining and enjoy collecting its specialist vocabulary, they may wish to research the process of draining water from the mines with pumps or extracting tin once the ore has been 'brought to grass'.

THOMAS AND HIS WISHES
Aims: to summarise key points of the story; to appreciate Thomas's growth in understanding by the time of his last wish; to add a further incident within the pattern of the story.
Teaching points: some children will need support to see that Thomas's last wish, because it is at last unselfish, brings about his eventual success and prosperity. If they suggest other interpretations of what happens, talk through the evidence with them and help

them to see that the story is implicitly a moral fable about thinking of others.

Extension: the story's moral is one which is common to many traditional tales, and indeed to much children's literature. The class or groups could discuss this message in fictional and real contexts.

A MESSAGE FROM THE BUCCAS

Aim: to reuse and/or invent archaic language in the style of the book.

Teaching points: most children will enjoy attempting the construction of a letter or poem in the author's style of speech, but it is not easy to do. A whole-class version should be possible. Discussion of how the patterning of stressed and unstressed syllables makes the line scan may be helpful.

Extension: some children may like to work on an appropriate handwriting (or font) and style of presentation for the Buccas' messages.

NO ONE BUT THOMAS

Aim: to reflect on one of the mysteries of the book and offer a personal opinion.

Teaching points: in their group or class discussion of this issue, children will reveal the extent to which they have appreciated the drift of the book. Their responses to the three offered explanations should go beyond stating a preference to evaluating the statements. The final illustration suggests that Thomas may no longer be able to see the Buccas.

Extension: the children's written opinions can be used as the basis of a class survey to show the range of opinion.

EVALUATION
WHAT DO YOU THINK?

Aims: to reconsider earlier hypotheses; to reassess the title and front cover illustration; to reflect on the experience of reading the book through writing comments.

Teaching points: make sure the children recognise that changes in their response to the book are signs of positive development, not of confusion or error. Group discussion of the questions can feed into whole-class debate. The picture on the front cover apparently relates to Chapter 4, but children may find discrepancies between this picture and the text. Provide a tape recorder for the final task.

Extension: another way of evaluating the book is to put the main characters, Thomas and Birdy, in the 'hot seat' and ask them questions about their lives. A further possible activity is for the children to plan a film of the book – deciding on the number of characters and scenes, the locations, lighting arrangements, dialogue, special effects and so on.

FURTHER READING

Other books by Jill Paton Walsh and illustrated by Alan Marks
Birdy and the Ghosties (Farrar, Straus and Giroux); *Matthew and the Sea Singer* (Simon and Schuster Young Books).

Other books by Jill Paton Walsh (mostly for older children)
A Parcel of Patterns (Puffin); *Fireweed* (Heinemann); *The Emperor's Winding Sheet* (Puffin); *A Chance Child* (Puffin); *Gaffer Sampson's Luck* (Puffin); *Goldengrove* (Puffin); *Unleaving* (Puffin); *Grace* (Puffin).

Other stories in which magic plays a part
Catkin by Antonia Barber, illus. Patrick Lynch (Walker Books)
The Fisherman and His Wife translated by Anthea Bell, illustrated by Alan Marks (Picture Book Studio)
The Tinderbox by Hans Christian Andersen, illustrated by Barry Moser (Little, Brown)

Other stories with a well-evoked historical setting
Sir Gawain and the Green Knight retold by Selina Hastings, illustrated by Juan Wijngaard (Walker Books)
One Thousand and One Arabian Nights retold by Geraldine McCaughrean, illustrated by Stephen Lewis (OUP)
Mufaro's Beautiful Daughters by John Steptoe (Puffin)

Other stories about the world of work
The People Who Could Fly retold by Virginia Hamilton, illustrated by Leo and Diane Dillon (Walker Books)
The Shoemaker and the Elves retold and illustrated by Cynthia and William Birrer (Hippo)
The White Crane retold and illustrated by Junko Morimoto (Collins)

Other stories illustrated by Alan Marks
The Green Children by Kevin Crossley-Holland (OUP)
Storm by Kevin Crossley-Holland (Heinemann)
David Copperfield by Charles Dickens (North/South Books)
King Arthur and the Round Table retold by Geraldine McCaughrean (Macdonald)